A WREATH OF CAROLS

47 CHRISTMAS SONGS
SELECTED AND EDITED BY
BETTY M. OWEN AND MARY E. MACEWEN

Piano arrangements and guitar chords by
Carla Bley and Mike Mantler

Illustrated by Paul Granger

SCHOLASTIC BOOK SERVICES

NEW YORK • LONDON • RICHMOND HILL, ONTARIO

Grateful acknowledgment is made for permission to use the following songs:

Every Star Shall Sing a Carol (page 68) is from SING ROUND THE YEAR, edited by Donald Swann, and published by David White Company. Used by permission of Essex Music, Inc., New York, N.Y.

Behold a Silly Tender Babe (page 16), lyrics by Robert Southwell, first appeared with the tune from *Corner's Geistliche Gesangbuch* in THE PENGUIN BOOK OF CHRISTMAS CAROLS, edited and arranged by Elizabeth Poston, and published by Penguin Books, Inc., Baltimore, Maryland.

On That Holy Midnight (page 29) and **We're Coming to Greet You** (page 18) are from AGUINALDOS DE PUERTO RICO, published by the Migration Division, Department of Labor, Commonwealth of Puerto Rico.

The Blessed Bird (page 36) is from NEW SONGS FOR THE JUNIOR CHOIR by Lee H. Bristol and Harold Friedall, published by Concordia Publishing House, St. Louis, Missouri.

A Christmas Carol (page 22) is from NINETEEN SONGS BY CHARLES IVES, published by Merion Music, Inc., Bryn Mawr, Pennsylvania.

The March of the Kings (page 44) lyrics are from THE PROGRESSIVE MUSIC SERIES, Book Two, published by Silver Burdett Company, Morristown, N.J.

A Scotch Lullaby (page 21) and **Cradle Song from Haiti** (page 24) are published by The H. W. Gray Company, New York, N.Y.

Jesús-Maria (page 40) is a new song, published for the first time in this book.

CONTENTS

Christmas Is Coming

Traditional English

With Spirit

1. Christ - mas is com - ing, The goose is get - ting fat!

Please to put a pen - ny in the old man's — hat!

Please to put a pen - ny in the old man's hat!

2.
If you have no penny,
A ha' penny will do,
If you have no ha' penny,
A farthing will do,
If you have no farthing,
Then God bless you.

We Wish You A Merry Christmas

Merrily

Traditional English

1. We wish you a Mer - ry Christ - mas, We wish you a Mer - ry Christ - mas, We wish you a Mer - ry Christ - mas, And a Hap - py New Year!

Refrain

Good ti - dings to you wher - ev - er you are; Good ti - dings for Christ - mas and a Hap - py New Year! We wish you a Mer - ry Christ - mas, We wish you a Mer - ry

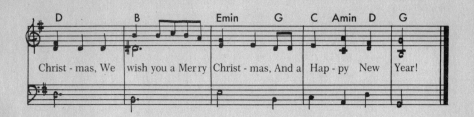

Christ - mas, We wish you a Merry Christ - mas, And a Hap - py New Year!

Joy To The World

Isaac Watts

Anonymous

1. Joy to the world! the Lord is come; Let earth re-ceive her King; Let ev-'ry heart pre-pare Him room And heav'n and na-ture sing, And heav'n and nature sing, And heav'n and heav'n and na-ture sing.

2.
Joy to the world! the Savior reigns;
Let men their songs employ;
While field and floods, rocks,
   hills and plains
Repeat the sounding joy,
Repeat the sounding joy,
Repeat, repeat the sounding joy.

3.
He rules the world with truth
   and grace
And makes the nations prove
The glories of His righteousness,
And wonders of His love,
And wonders of His love,
And wonders, and wonders
   of His love.

The First Nowell

Traditional English

Moderately

1. The first Nowell, the angel did say, Was to certain poor shepherds in fields as they lay; In fields where they lay keeping their sheep. On a cold winter's night that was so deep.

Refrain

Nowell, Nowell, Nowell, Nowell,

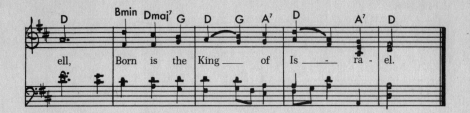

ell, Born is the King ___ of Is ___ ra - el.

2.
They looked up and saw a Star
Shining in the East, beyond
   them far;
And to the earth it gave great light,
And so it continued both
   day and night.
      Nowell, Nowell, etc.

3.
This star drew nigh to the
   North-West,
O'er Bethlehem it took its rest,
And there it did both stop and stay
Right over the place where
   Jesus lay.
      Nowell, Nowell, etc.

4.
Then enter'd in those Wisemen
   three,
Full rev'rently on bended knee,
And offer'd there in His presence,
Their gold and myrrh and
   frankincense.
      Nowell, Nowell, etc.

O Christmas Tree

Traditional German

2.
O Christmas tree, O Christmas
  tree,
Of all the trees most lovely;
Each year, you bring to me delight
Gleaming in the Christmas light.
O Christmas tree, O Christmas
  tree,
Of all the trees most lovely.

3.
O Christmas tree, O Christmas
  tree,
Your leaves will teach me, also,
That hope and love and
  faithfulness
Are precious things I can possess.
O Christmas tree, O Christmas
  tree,
Your leaves will teach me, also.

Go Tell It On The Mountain

Traditional
Negro Spiritual

1. When I was a seek - er, I sought both night and day; I asked the Lord to help me, And He showed me the way.

Refrain Slow March Tempo

Go tell it on the moun - tain, O - ver the hills and ev - 'ry - where;

Go tell it on the moun - tain, That Je - sus Christ is born.

2.
He made me a watchman,
Upon the city wall;
And if I am a Christian,
I am the least of all.
        Go tell it on the mountain, etc.

15

Behold A Silly Tender Babe

Robert Southwell

David Gregor Corner
arranged by Elizabeth Poston

With an easy, gentle swing

1. Be - hold _ a sil - ly ten - der Babe In freez - ing win - ter night _ In home - ly man - ger trem - bling lies, A - las a pi - teous sight, _ a - las, _ a pi - teous sight. _

4. The per - sons in that poor at - tire His roy - al li - v'ries wear, _ The Prince is come from heav'n, Him - self is priz - ed This pomp

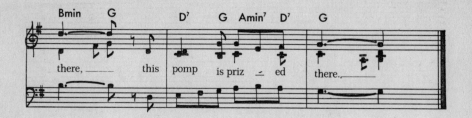

there, _____ this pomp is priz - ed there., _____

2.
The inns are full, no man will yield
This little Pilgrim bed;
But forced He is with silly beasts
In crib to shroud His head.

3.
This stable is a Prince's court,
The crib His chair of state:
The beasts are parcel of His pomp,
The wooden dish His plate.

5.
With joy approach, O Christian
    wight,
Do homage to the King;
And highly praise His humble
    pomp
Which He from heaven doth bring.

We're Coming To Greet You

Puerto Rican
Aguinaldo

1. We're com - ing to greet you, this ho - li - day gay, We're com - ing to greet you, this ho - li - day gay, With sun - shine and mu - sic to bright - en the way, With sun - shine and mus - sic to bright - en the way.

2.
So welcome us, please, with some holiday cheer,
So welcome us, please, with some holiday cheer,
Tis Christmas, the happiest time of the year,
Tis Christmas, the happiest time of the year.

While Shepherds Watched Their Flocks

Nahum Tate
Moderately

George F. Händel

2.
"Fear not!" said he for mighty
   dread
Had seized their troubled mind,
"Glad tidings of great joy I bring,
To you and all mankind,
To you and all mankind.

3.
"To you, in David's town this day,
Is born of David's line,
The Savior Who is Christ the Lord;
And this shall be the sign,
And this shall be the sign:

4.
"The heavenly Babe you there
   shall find
To human view displayed,
All meanly wrapped in swathing
   bands,
And in a manger laid,
And in a manger laid."

Away In A Manger

Anonymous

James R. Murray

2.

The cattle are lowing, the Baby awakes,
But little Lord Jesus, no crying He makes.
I love Thee, Lord Jesus, look down from the sky,
And stay by my cradle till morning is nigh.

3.

Be near me, Lord Jesus, I ask Thee to stay
Close by me forever, and love me, I pray.
Bless all the dear children in Thy tender care,
And fit us for Heaven to live with Thee there.

A Scotch Lullaby

John J. Moment

Scotch Air

1. Wee lamb in the heath-er, a-lone and a-cold, How cam' ye to wan-der sae far frae the fold? Though harsh blows the night wind, and dread wi' a-larms, Ha' done wi' your greet-ing, come, rest in my arms.

2.
Wee Bairn in the manger, how
    cam' Ye to lie
Whaur only the oxen attend to
    Your cry?
Wad naebody mak' Ye a bonny
    wee bed,
Naebody a pillow, snawwhite,
    for Your head?

A Christmas Carol

Traditional

Charles Ives

will ___ to ___ men! _____ No _____ el! _____

2.
O'er the cradle of a King,
Hear the Angels sing:
In Excelsis Gloria, Gloria!
From His Father's home on high,
Lo! for us He came to die;
Hear the Angels sing:
Venite adoremus Dominum.

Cradle Song From Haiti

Helen A. Dickinson

Traditional

Slowly

1. Je - su! Lit - tle Babe so fair, Je - su! In the man-ger there, An - gels guard Thy sleep. And Thy mo-ther o'er Thy crib ten-der-ly her watch doth keep. Je-su! Thou dear Babe di - vine.

2.
Jesu! Wise men came from far,
Jesu! Guided by the star;
Humbly Thee they sought,
Gold and incense sweet, rich gifts
From the East to Thee they
    brought.
Jesu! Thou dear Babe divine.

3.
Jesu! Come we now to Thee,
Jesu! Lowly bend the knee:
We Thy grace implore;
Lord, we too, with childlike hearts,
At the manger Thee adore.
Jesu! Thou dear Babe divine.

I Heard The Bells On Christmas Day

Henry W. Longfellow

J. Baptiste Calkin

2.
I thought how, as the day had
   come,
The belfries of all Christendom
Had roll'd along th'unbroken song
Of peace on earth, good will
   to men.

3.
And in despair I bow'd my head:
"There is no peace on earth,"
   I said,
"For hate is strong and mocks
   the song
Of peace on earth, good will
   to men."

4.
Then pealed the bells more loud and deep: .
"God is not dead, nor doth He sleep:
The wrong shall fail, the right prevail,
With peace on earth, good will to men."

The Twelve Days Of Christmas

Traditional English

1. On the first day of Christ-mas my true love sent to me A par-tridge___ in a pear tree.

2. On the sec-ond day of Christmas my true love sent to me Two tur-tle doves and a par-tridge___ in a pear tree.

3. On the third day of Christ-mas my true love sent to me Three French___ hens, two tur-tle doves and a par-tridge___ in a pear

7.
On the seventh day of Christmas,
my true love sent to me:
Seven swans a-swimming,

8.
On the eighth day of Christmas,
my true love sent to me:
Eight maids a-milking,

9.
On the ninth day of Christmas,
my true love sent to me:
Nine ladies dancing,

10.
On the tenth day of Christmas,
my true love sent to me:
Ten lords a-leaping,

11.
On the eleventh day of Christmas,
my true love sent to me:
Eleven pipers piping,

12.
On the twelfth day of Christmas,
my true love sent to me:
Twelve drummers drumming,

On That Holy Midnight

Puerto Rican
Aguinaldo

Brightly Refrain

La la la la la la la la la la la la la la la la la la la

la la la la la la la la la la la la la la

1. On that Ho - ly Mid - night when our Lord was born,

All the cocks were crow - ing, gai - ly, as for dawn.

Refrain
2.
On that Holy Evening
In the lonely night,
Came to earth our Savior,
Christ, the King of Light.

O Come, O Come, Emmanuel

Latin

Advent Carol
Plainsong

1. O come, O come, Em-man-u-el, And ran-som cap-tive Is-ra-el, That mourns in lone-ly ex-ile here, Un-til the Son of God ap-pear. Re-joice, re-joice, Em-man-u-el, Shall come to Thee, O Is-ra-el.

2.
O come, Thou Dayspring, come
   and cheer
Our spirits by Thine advent here;
Disperse the gloomy clouds of
   night,
And death's dark shadows put
   to flight.
     Rejoice, rejoice, Emmanuel,
       etc.

3.
O come, Thou Key of David, come,
And open wide our heav'nly home;
Make safe the way that leads on
   high,
And close the path to misery.
     Rejoice, rejoice, Emmanuel,
       etc.

The Three Kings

John H. Hopkins

1. We three kings of O - ri - ent are;

Bear - ing gifts, we trav - erse a - far

Field and foun - tain, moor and moun - tain,

Fol - low - ing yon - der star.

O —

star of won - der, star of night,

32

Star with roy - al beau - ty bright,
West - ward lead - ing still pro - ceed - ing,
Guide us to Thy per - fect light.

2.
Born a King on Bethlehem's plain,
Gold I bring, to crown Him again,
King forever, ceasing never,
Over us all to reign.
    O star of wonder, etc.

3.
Frankincense to offer have I,
Incense owns a Deity nigh.
Pray'r and praising all men
    raising,
Worship Him, God most high.
      O star of wonder, etc.

4.
Myrrh is mine, its bitter perfume
Breathes a life of gathering gloom;
Sorrowing, sighing, bleeding,
    dying,
Sealed in the stone cold tomb.
    O star of wonder, etc.

5.
Glorious now behold Him arise,
King and God and Sacrifice,
Alleluia, Alleluia,
Earth to the heav'ns replies.
      O star of wonder, etc.

Bring A Torch, Jeannette, Isabella

Lively

Traditional French

1. Bring a torch, _____ Jean - nette, Is - a - bel - la, Bring a torch, to the cra _____ dle run! It is Je - sus, good folk of the vil - lage; Christ _____ is born and Ma - ry's call - ing: Ah! ah! beau - ti - ful

is the Moth - er, Ah! ah!

beau - ti - ful is Her Son!

2.
It is wrong when the Child is
  sleeping,
It is wrong to talk so loud;
Silence, all, as you gather around,
Lest your noise should waken
  Jesus:
Hush! hush! see how fast He
  slumbers;
Hush! hush! see how fast He
  sleeps!

3.
Softly to the little stable,
Softly for a moment come;
Look and see how charming is
  Jesus,
How He is white, His cheeks are
  rosy!
Hush! hush! see how the Child is
  sleeping;
Hush! hush! see how He smiles in
  dreams.

The Blessed Bird

Words from the flyleaf
of a 16th-century prayerbook

music
by Lee Hastings Bristol, Jr.

hem. "Nowe where is he of Da-vid's line?" She
harm, "Nowe bless-ed be the gen-tle storke For

asked at house, and halle, "He is not here," they
ev-er more," quoth He "For that she saw my

spoke hard-ly, "But in a maun-gier stalle." 2. She
sadde es-tate And show-ed such pi-

2. Full wel-come shall she ev-er be In ham-let and in

halle, And called henceforth the bless-ed bird And friend to ba-bies all."

O Come, All Ye Faithful

Old Latin Hymn

2.
Sing, choirs of angels, sing in
exultation,
Sing, all ye citizens of heav'n
above!
Glory to God, all glory in the
highest!
    O come, let us adore Him, etc.

3.
Yea, Lord, we greet Thee, born this
holy morning,
Jesus, to Thee be glory giv'n!
Word of the Father, now in flesh
appearing:
    O come, let us adore Him, etc.

Jesús–Maria

J. Friedman

Carla Bley

Gather Around The Christmas Tree

Traditional English

1. Gather a-round the Christ-mas tree! Gather a-round the Christ-mas tree! Evergreen have its bran-ches been; It is King of all the wood-land scene. For Christ, our King, is born to-day! His reign shall nev-er pass a-way, Ho-san-na, Ho-san-na, Ho-san-na in the high-est!

2.
Gather around the Christmas tree!
Gather around the Christmas tree!
Once the pride of the mountainside,
Now cut down to grace our
   Christmastide:
For Christ from Heav'n to earth
   came down,
To gain, through death, a nobler crown.
   Hosanna, Hosanna,
   Hosanna, in the highest!

3.
Gather around the Christmas tree!
Gather around the Christmas tree!
Ev'ry bough has a burden now;
They are gifts of love for us, we
   trow.
For Christ is born, His love to
   show,
And give good gifts to men below.
   Hosanna, Hosanna,
   Hosanna, in the highest!

Silent Night

Joseph Mohr

Franz Gruber

Gently

1. Si - lent night, Ho - ly night, All is calm, All is bright, Round yon vir — gin Moth-er and child. Ho - ly In - fant so ten - der and mild, Sleep in heav - en - ly peace, Sleep — in heav - en - ly peace!

2.
Silent night, holy night,
Shepherds quake at the sight;
Glories stream from heaven afar,
Heavenly hosts sing *alleluia,*
Christ, the Savior is born!
Christ, the Savior is born!

3.
Silent night, holy night,
Son of God, love's pure light
Radiant beams from Thy holy face,
With the dawn of redeeming grace,
Jesus Lord, at Thy Birth,
Jesus Lord, at Thy Birth.

The March Of The Kings

Abbie Farwell Brown
(from the French)

Provencal Melody

1. Yes - ter - day I met up - on the way, The three great Kings who came from for - eign re _ gions. Yes - ter - day I met up - on the way, The three great Kings in all their fine ar - ray. With chests of gold and of gifts un - told, then came the hosts of the marching mighty Le - gions; with chests of gold and of gifts un - told, the three great Kings in all their fine ar - ray.

2.
Christmas Day they went upon their way,
The three great Kings with all the precious treasure.
Christmas Day they went upon their way
To seek a Baby lying in the hay.
The one a black King, and one was brown,
Who came so far for a little Baby's pleasure;
And one was white with a golden crown,
The three great Kings so gallant and so gay!

Good King Wenceslas

John M. Neale

Traditional English

Moderately

2.
"Hither, page, and stand by me,
If thou know'st it; telling,
Yonder peasant, who is he?
Where and what his dwelling?"
"Sire, he lives a good league hence,
Underneath the mountain;
Right against the forest fence,
By Saint Agnes' fountain."

3.

"Bring me flesh, and bring me
    wine,
Bring me pine logs hither;
Thou and I will see him dine,
When we bear him thither."
Page and monarch forth they
    went,
Forth they went together;
Through the rude wind's wild
    lament,
And the bitter weather.

4.

"Sire, the night is darker now,
And the wind blows stronger;
Fails my heart, I know not how,
I can go no longer."
"Mark my footsteps, my good page,
Tread thou in them boldly:
Thou shalt find the winter's rage,
Freeze thy blood less coldly."

5.

In his master's steps he trod,
Where the snow lay dinted;
Heat was in the very sod
Which the saint had printed.
Therefore, Christian men, be sure,
Wealth or rank possessing,
Ye who now will bless the poor,
Shall yourselves find blessing.

Rise Up, Shepherd, And Follow

Traditional
Negro Spiritual

Fol - low the star of Beth - le - hem, ___ Rise up, shep - herd, and fol - low. ___

2.
If you take good heed to the angel's word,
Rise up, shepherd, and follow
You'll forget your flock, you'll forget your herd;
Rise up, Shepherd, and follow.
      Leave your ewes and leave your lambs, etc.

Beside Thy Cradle

Old German Melody
harmonized by J. S. Bach

Be - side Thy cra - dle here I stand, O Thou that ev - er liv - est, And bring Thee with a will - ing hand The ver - y gifts Thou giv - est. Ac - cept me; 'tis my mind and heart, My soul, my strength, my ev - 'ry part. That Thou from me re - quir - est.

Angels From The Realms Of Glory

James Montgomery

Henry Smart

Moderately

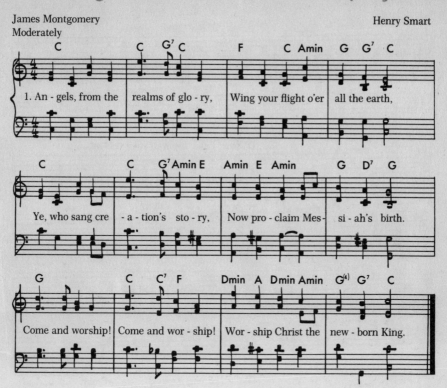

1. An - gels, from the realms of glo - ry, Wing your flight o'er all the earth,
Ye, who sang cre - a - tion's sto - ry, Now pro - claim Mes - si - ah's birth.
Come and worship! Come and wor - ship! Wor - ship Christ the new - born King.

2.
Shepherds in the field abiding,
Watching o'er your flocks by night,
God with man is now residing,
Yonder shines the infant Light.
Come and worship! etc.

3.
Sages, leave your contemplations,
Brighter visions beam afar;
Seek the great Desire of nations
Ye have seen His natal star.
Come and worship! etc.

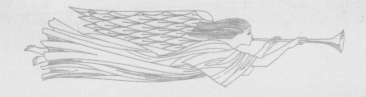

What Child Is This?

William Dix

Old English Air

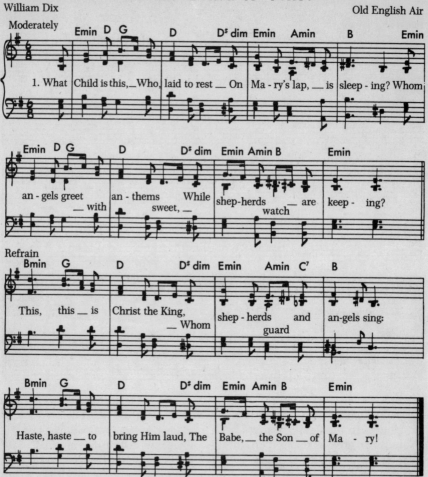

2.

Why lies He in such mean estate,
Where ox and ass are feeding?
Good Christian, fear: for sinners here
The silent Word is pleading.
Nails, spear, shall pierce Him through,
The Cross be borne, for me, for you:
Hail, hail, the Word made flesh,
The Babe, the Son of Mary!

3.

So bring Him incense, gold and myrrh,
Come peasant, king to own Him,
The King of kings, salvation brings,
Let loving hearts enthrone Him.
Raise, raise, the song on high,
The Virgin sings her lullaby:
Joy, joy, for Christ is born,
The Babe, the Son of Mary.

Deck The Halls

Traditional Welsh

Gaily

1. Deck the halls with boughs of hol-ly Fa la la la la, la la la la,

'Tis the sea-son to be jol-ly, Fa la la la la, la la la la.

Don we now our gay ap-par-rel, Fa _ la la _ la la la la,

Troll the an-cient Yule-tide car-ol, Fa la la la la, la la la la.

2.
See the blazing Yule before us,
    Fa la la, etc.
Strike the harp and join the
    chorus,
    Fa la la, etc.
Follow me in merry measure,
    Fa la la, etc.
While I tell of Yuletide treasure,
    Fa la la, etc.

3.
Fast away the old year passes,
    Fa la la, etc.
Hail the new, ye lads and lasses,
    Fa la la, etc.
Sing we joyous all together,
    Fa la la, etc.
Heedless of the wind and weather,
    Fa la la, etc.

Angels We Have Heard On High

Traditional French

Joyously

1. An - gels we have heard on high, Sweet - ly sing - ing o'er the plains And the moun - tains in re - ply, Ech - o - ing their joy - ous strains.

Refrain

Glo - ri - a. in ex - cel - sis De - o Glo - ri - a in ex - cel - sis De - o.

2.
Shepherds why this jubilee?
Why your joyous strains prolong?
What the gladsome tidings be
Which inspire your heav'nly song?
Gloria in excelsis Deo
Gloria in excelsis Deo.

3.
Come to Bethlehem and see
Him whose birth the angels sing;
Come, adore on bended knee,
Christ the Lord the new born King.
Gloria in excelsis Deo
Gloria in excelsis Deo.

4.
See Him in a manger laid
Whom the choirs of angels praise;
Mary, Joseph, lend your aid,
While our hearts in love we raise.
Gloria in excelsis Deo
Gloria in excelsis Deo.

I Saw Three Ships

Traditional English

Gaily

1. I saw three ships come sail - ing in. On Christ - mas Day, on Christ - mas Day; I saw three ships come sail - ing in, On Christ - mas Day in the morn - - ing.

2.
And what was in those ships all three?
On Christmas Day, on Christmas Day,
And what was in those ships all three?
On Christmas Day in the morning.

3.
Our Savior Christ and His lady.
On Christmas Day, on Christmas Day;
Our Savior Christ and His lady,
On Christmas Day in the morning.

4.
Pray, whither sailed those ships all three?
On Christmas Day, on Christmas Day;
Pray, whither sailed those ships all three?
On Christmas Day in the morning.

5.
O, they sailed in to Bethlehem,
On Christmas Day, on Christmas Day;
O, they sailed in to Bethlehem,
On Christmas Day in the morning.

6.
And all the bells on earth shall
  ring,
On Christmas Day, on Christmas
  Day,
And all the bells on earth shall
  ring,
On Christmas Day in the morning.

7.
And all the angels in Heav'n shall
  sing,
On Christmas Day, on Christmas
  Day,
And all the angels in Heav'n shall
  sing,
On Christmas Day in the morning.

8.
And all the souls on earth shall
  sing,
On Christmas Day, on Christmas
  Day,
And all the souls on earth shall
  sing,
On Christmas Day in the morning.

9.
Then let us all rejoice amain!
On Christmas Day, on Christmas
  Day,
Then let us all rejoice amain!
On Christmas Day in the morning.

Children, Go Where I Send Thee

Traditional Negro Spiritual

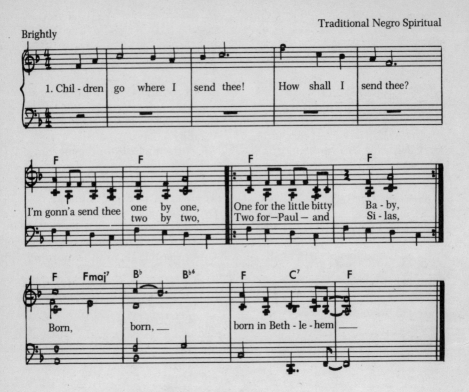

Three for the Hebrew children,

Four for the four that stood at the door,

Five for the gospel preachers,

Six for the six that never got fixed,

Sev'n for the sev'n that never went to Heav'n

Eight for the eight that stood at the gate,

Nine for the nine that dressed so fine,

Ten for the Ten Commandments.

Let All Mortal Flesh Keep Silence

Solemnly

French Advent Carol

1. Let all mor - tal flesh keep si - lence, and with fear and trem - bling stand; Ponder noth - ing earth - ly mind - ed, for with blessing in His hand, Christ our God to earth de - scend - eth, our full hom - age to de - mand.

2.
King of kings, yet born of Mary, as of old on earth He stood,
Lord of lords, in human vesture—in the Body and the Blood—
He will give to all the faithful His own Self for heavenly Food.

3.
Rank on rank the host of heaven spreads its vanguard on the way,
As the Light of Light descendeth from the realms of endless day,
That the powers of hell may vanish as the darkness clears away.

4.
At His feet the six-winged seraph; cherubim with sleepless eye,
Veil their faces to the Presence, as with ceaseless voice they cry,
Alleluia, alleluia, alleluia, Lord most high.

O Little Town Of Bethlehem

Phillip Brooks

Lewis H. Redner

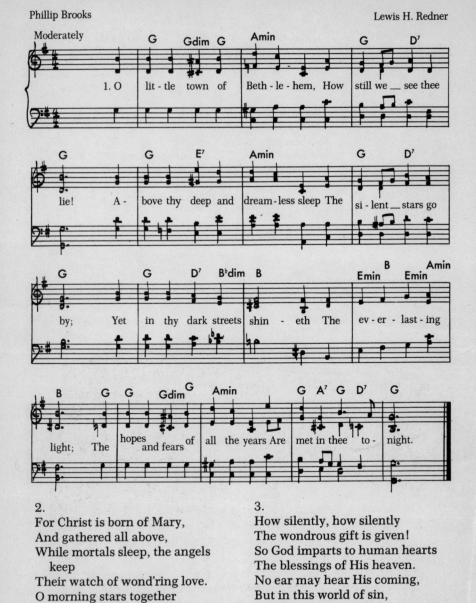

2.

For Christ is born of Mary,
And gathered all above,
While mortals sleep, the angels
keep
Their watch of wond'ring love.
O morning stars together
Proclaim the holy birth,
And praises sing to God the King,
And peace to men on earth!

3.

How silently, how silently
The wondrous gift is given!
So God imparts to human hearts
The blessings of His heaven.
No ear may hear His coming,
But in this world of sin,
Where meek souls will receive Him
still,
The dear Christ enters in.

4.
O holy Child of Bethlehem!
Descend to us, we pray;
Cast out our sin and enter in,
Be born in us today.
We hear the Christmas angels
The great glad tidings tell;
O come to us, abide with us,
Our Lord Immanuel!

The Holly And The Ivy

Traditional English

2.
The holly bears a blossom,
As white as lily flow'r,
And Mary bore sweet Jesus Christ,
To be our dear Savior:
 The rising of the sun, etc.

3.
The holly bears a berry,
As red as any blood,
And Mary bore sweet Jesus Christ,
To do poor sinners good:
 The rising of the sun, etc.

4.
The holly bears a prickle,
As sharp as any thorn,
And Mary bore sweet Jesus Christ,
On Christmas day in the morn:
 The rising of the sun, etc.

5.
The holly bears a bark,
As bitter as the gall,
And Mary bore sweet Jesus Christ,
For to redeem us all:
 The rising of the sun, etc.

6.
The holly and the ivy,
When they are both full grown,
Of all the trees that are in the
 wood,
The holly bears the crown:
 The rising of the sun, etc.

Hark! The Herald Angels Sing

Charles Wesley

Felix Mendelssohn

2.
Christ, by highest heav'n adored;
Christ, the everlasting Lord;
Late in time behold Him come,
Offspring of the Virgin's womb.
Veil'd in flesh the Godhead see;
Hail th'Incarnate Deity,
Pleased as Man with man to dwell,
Jesus, our Emmanuel!
    Hark! the herald angels sing, etc.

3.
Mild He lays His glory by,
Born that man no more may die,
Born to raise the sons of earth,
Born to give them second birth.
Ris'n with healing in His wings,
Light and life to all He brings,
Hail the Son of Righteousness!
Hail, the heav'n born Prince of
    Peace!
    Hark! the herald angels sing, etc.

Good Christian Men, Rejoice

Old German

Spirited

1. Good Chris - tian men, re - joice _____ With
heart, and soul, and voice; _____ Give ye heed to
what we say: News! News! Je - sus Christ is
born to - day! Ox and ass be - fore Him bow, And
He is in the man - ger now; Christ is born to -

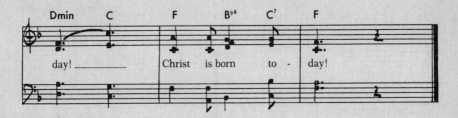

day! _____ Christ is born to - day!

2.
Good Christian men, rejoice
With heart, and soul, and voice;
Now ye hear of endless bliss:
Joy! Joy!
Jesus Christ was born for this!
He hath ope'd the heav'nly door,
And man is blessed evermore;
Christ was born for this!
Christ was born for this!

3.
Good Christian men, rejoice
With heart, and soul, and voice;
Now ye need not fear the grave:
Peace! Peace!
Jesus Christ was born to save!
Calls you one and calls you all,
To gain His everlasting hall;
Christ was born to save!
Christ was born to save!

Every Star Shall Sing A Carol

words and music by
Sydney Carter

Gently, but not slow

Ev - ry star shall sing a car - ol!

Ev - 'ry creature __ high or __ low, Come and praise the King of Heav - en

By what-ev - er __ name you know. God a - bove, Man be - low,

Verses 1 to 5
Ho - ly is the __ name I __ know.

Last time
Ho - ly is the __ name I __ know.

2.
When the King of all creation
Had a cradle on the earth,
Holy was the human body,
Holy was the human birth.
    God above, Man below,
    Holy is the name I know.

3.
Who can tell what other cradle
High above the milky way
Still may rock the King of Heaven
On another Christmas Day?
    God above, Man below,
    Holy is the name I know.

4.
Who can count how many crosses
Still to come or long ago
Crucify the King of Heaven?
Holy is the name I know.
    God above, Man below,
    Holy is the name I know.

5.
Who can tell what other body
He will hallow for His own?
I will praise the Son of Mary,
Brother of my blood and bone.
    God above, Man below,
    Holy is the name I know.

6.
Every star and every planet,
Every creature high and low,
Come and praise the King of
    Heaven
By whatever name you know.
    God above, Man below,
    Holy is the name I know.

God Rest You Merry, Gentlemen

Traditional English

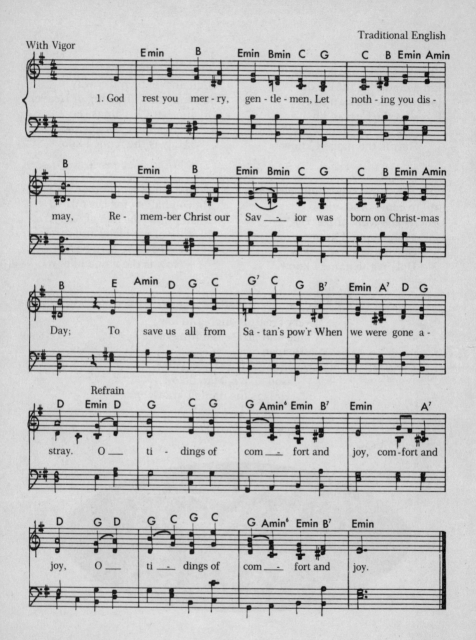

2.
In Bethlehem, in Jewry,
This blessed Babe was born,
And laid within a manger
Upon this blessed morn;
The which His Mother Mary,
Did nothing take in scorn.
    O tidings of comfort and joy, etc.

3.
From God our heav'nly Father,
A blessed angel came;
And unto certain shepherds
Brought tidings of the same;
How that in Bethlehem was born
The Son of God by Name.
    O tidings of comfort and joy, etc.

It Came Upon The Midnight Clear

Edmund H. Sears

Richard S. Willis

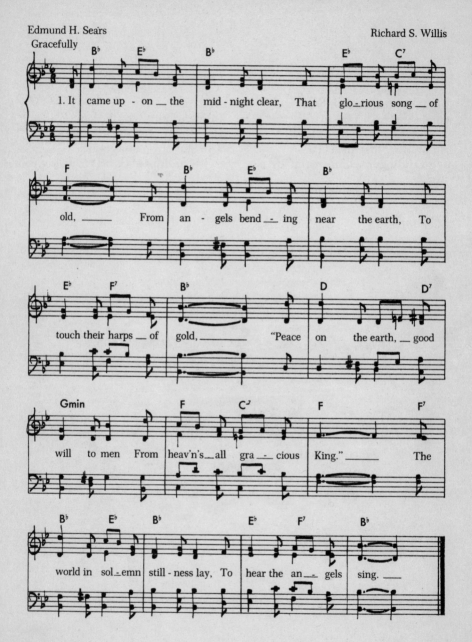

x

1. It came up-on the mid-night clear, That glo-rious song of old, From an-gels bend-ing near the earth, To touch their harps of gold, "Peace on the earth, good will to men From heav'n's all gra-cious King." The world in sol-emn still-ness lay, To hear the an-gels sing.

2.
Still through the cloven skies, they
   come,
With peaceful wings unfurl'd,
And still their heav'nly music
   floats
O'er all the weary world:
Above its sad and lowly plains
They bend on hov'ring wing,
And ever o'er its Babel sounds
The blessed angels sing.

3.
O ye, beneath life's crushing load,
Whose forms are bending low,
Who toil along the climbing way
With painful steps and slow:
Look now, for glad and golden
   hours
Come swiftly on the wing;
O rest beside the weary road
And hear the angels sing.

4.
For lo! the days are hast'ning on,
By prophets seen of old,
When with the ever-circling years,
Shall come the time foretold,
When peace shall over all the earth
Its ancient splendors fling,
And the whole world send back the song
Which now the angels sing.

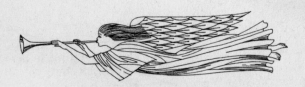

Coventry Carol

Robert Croo

Traditional English

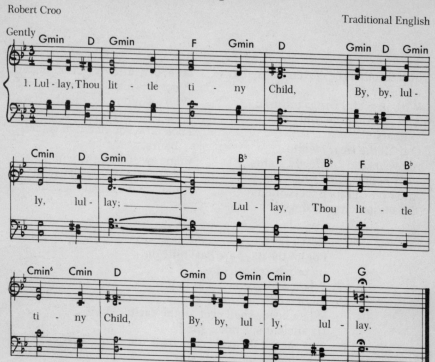

1. Lul - lay, Thou lit - tle ti - ny Child, By, by, lul - ly, lul - lay; Lul - lay, Thou lit - tle ti - ny Child, By, by, lul - ly, lul - lay.

2.
O sisters, too, how may we do,
For to preserve this day;
This poor Youngling for Whom we
    sing,
By, by, lully, lullay.

3.
Herod the King, in his raging,
Charged he hath this day;
His men of might, in his own sight,
All children young, to slay.

4.
Then woe is me, poor Child, for
    Thee,
And ever mourn and say;
For Thy parting nor say nor sing,
By, by, lully, lullay.

What You Gonna Call Yo' Pretty Little Baby?

Traditional Negro Spiritual

Some call Him one thing, I'll call Him Jesus.
Sweet little baby, born in a manger.

Wassail Song

2.
We are not daily beggars
That go from door to door,
But we are neighbors' children
Whom you have seen before:
    Love and joy come to you, etc.

3.
We have got a little purse
Of stretching leather skin;
We want a little money,
To line it well within:
    Love and joy come to you, etc.

4.
God bless the master of this house,
Likewise the mistress too;
And all the little children,
That 'round the table go:
    Love and joy come to you, etc.

5.
Good master and good mistress,
While you're sitting by the fire,
Pray think of us poor children
Who wander in the mire:
    Love and joy come to you, etc.

Lo, How A Rose E'er Blooming

Old German Melody
(harmonized by Michael Praetorius)

1. Lo, how a Rose e'er bloom - ing From ten - der stem hath sprung! Of Jes - se's lin - eage com - ing, As men of old have sung. It came, a flow - 'ret bright, A - mid the cold of win - ter, When half - spent was the night.

2.
Isaiah 'twas foretold it,
The Rose I have in mind,
With Mary we behold it,
The Virgin Mother kind.
To show God's love aright,
She bore to men a Savior
When half-spent was the night.

3.
This Flow'r, whose fragrance tender
With sweetness fills the air,
Dispels with glorious splendor
The darkness ev'rywhere.
True man, yet very God;
From sin and death He saves us,
And lightens ev'ry load.

All My Heart This Night Rejoices

Paulus Gerhardt

Horatio Parker

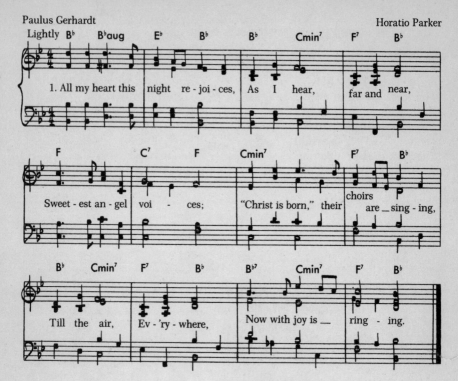

1. All my heart this night re-joi-ces, As I hear, far and near, Sweet-est an-gel voi - ces; "Christ is born," their choirs are — sing-ing, Till the air, Ev - 'ry - where, Now with joy is __ ring - ing.

2.
Hark! a voice from yonder manger,
Soft and sweet, doth entreat,
"Flee from woe and danger.
Brethren, come; from all that
  grieves you,
You are freed,
All you need I will surely give you."

3.
Come, then, let us hasten yonder;
Here let all, great and small,
Kneel in awe and wonder.
Love Him who with love is
  yearning,
Hail the star
That from far
Bright with hope is burning!